FOREWORD
By the Fat Controller, alias Paul Edwards

When Jim rang me up to ask me to write this foreword, I was in the middle of clearing up breakfast on the first day of testing in Estoril in November.

I am sure all of you motor racing fans will enjoy the cartoons in this edition, as I know that some of them have not made the pages of the comics because they have been too political. I myself have borne the brunt of Jim's cartoons on more than one occasion, as have many well known motor racing personalities and I am sure this book will give continued enjoyment to all the racing enthusiasts around the world.

Jim is well known for upsetting people with his cartoons, but also for bringing immense enjoyment. I hope he continues to do this for the foreseeable future because I know that there are thousands of people who turn first to the letters and editorial page of Autosport to see who Jim's had a go at this week.

Let's hope that Jim carries on having a go at us, as we must try and laugh at ourselves in adversity – and there is always plenty of that in motorsport!

The Fat Controller
alias Paul Edwards
Williams Grand Prix Engineering

Acknowledgements

To Cars and Car Conversions, What Car,
Racecar Engineering, Carsport.
Many thanks to the lads at Autosport who have thought up
some quite funny ideas this year, none of which I used of course, and
to Peter 'red pen' Foubister-he knows why! To Andrew 'smarty pants' Benson,
who took a lot of stick from a lot of people, including me,
and who was right all along. Last but not least,to designer
Fabio Taglioni for my Ducati.

Thomas Tebbutt age 9

"There's a fine line between fishing and just standing on the shore like an idiot"

I must have crystal balls, the original of this was dated; December, **1995!**

Mark Blundell suffering the swings and roundabouts of outrageous fortune

9

Jeremy Clarkson, the 'outstanding' star of the Autosport International show.

Sorry Mark, this _is_ cruel, look, let me get you a drink.........ice?

13

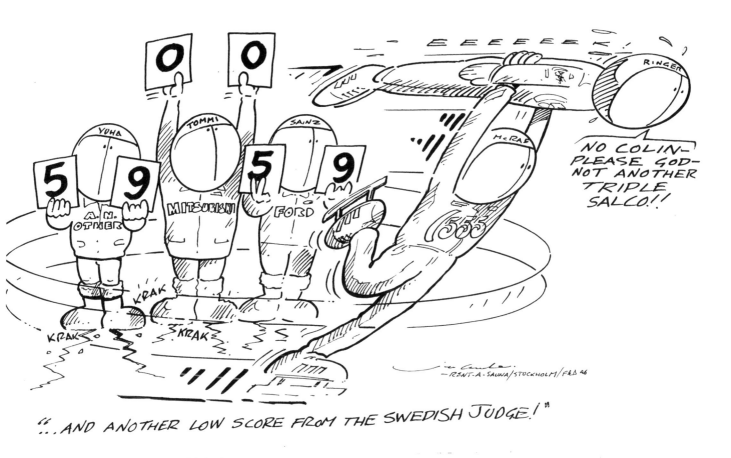

"...AND ANOTHER LOW SCORE FROM THE SWEDISH JUDGE!"

World Rally Champion Colin McRae had a quiet year by his standards and, yes,
he did drop his co-driver

15

The annual meeting of the "Don't Like World Championship Rallying Society"

17

"The Navy Lark" comes to Formula One, when an ex Polaris nuclear submarine
captain is appointed race director

19

Just wishful thinking

There were rumours all year that Gary Lineker's favourite team were moving to Dublin

Both of the lads had tumbles only weeks after this was in Autosport; Martin did a few somersaults in Melbourne and Mark had a huge accident in Brazil

25

A new term was beginning and the school bus to Melbourne was packed

Oh dear, not even bronze this year for the Jordan team

These guys are from another planet. Brundle has a major accident in Melbourne and then runs, yes actually runs, to get in the spare car

31

Following Brundle's crash test in Melbourne all the muttering about Jordan's interpretation of the new cockpit design faded away

33

34

Looks like the Arrows jokes are going to run and run

35

Wow! At the start of the season it all looked <u>so</u> easy

37

ARGENTINA — THE McLAREN DE-BRIEF!!

During the Argentine Grand Prix, Coulthard was overtaken by an Arrows
.......Arrows.......get it? Good, because it had to be explained to David

39

Don't worry, knowing Bernie I'm sure he's got some veggie burgers out the back somewhere

Remember, what goes up, comes down

43

All year the Germans got to the beach first

45

Well done David, safe from all the slings and arrows

At Imola Alesi was no longer the Tifosi's favourite son

49

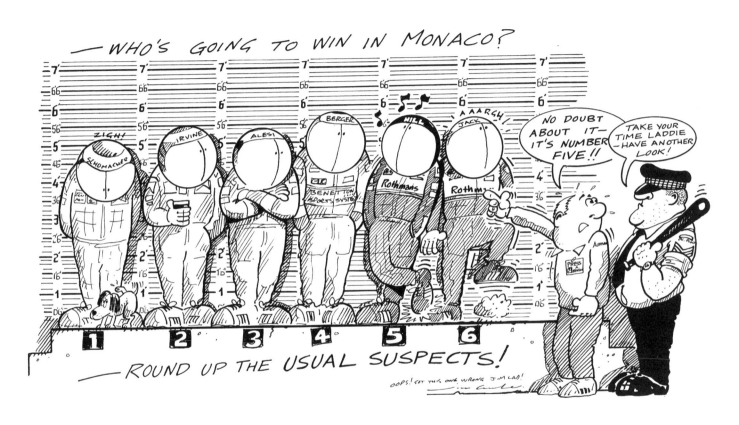

Oh dear, how wrong can you get?

The lads from Arrows bought the original of this. Well it <u>was</u> their car!

The Pepsi/Cola war was in full swing as the two Indy camps did their 'thang'

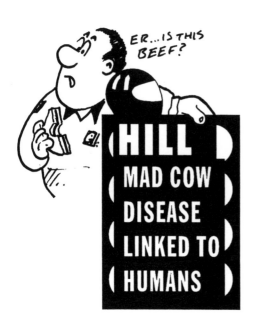

"Call me '**Moses**' Schumacher"- leading his people into the promised land

Did anybody actually go to Le Mans this year?

It's true, Hans Stuck yodels when he wins a race. Krazy Kraut!

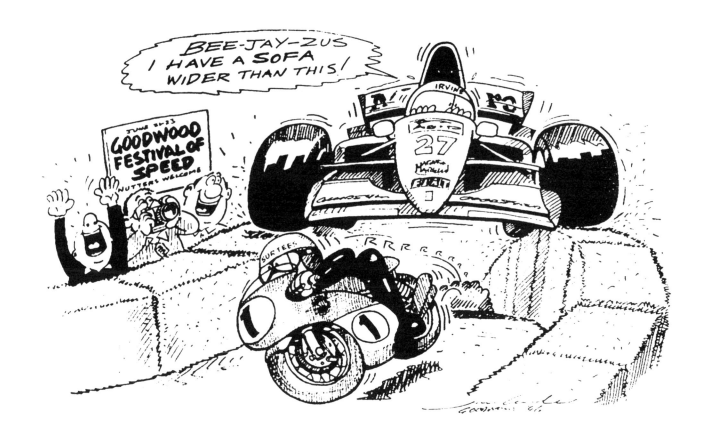

Eddeeee Irvine, one of the many stars at Goodwood

64

Not quite the forgotten hero

65

Martin Whitaker arrived at Ford this year, watch out Henry he'll be after <u>your</u> job next

Klinsmann scored more than Ferrari this year!

Ha, ha, this was drawn the week before the Grand Prix. It's those crystal balls again

Enzo would have hung them all out to dry

My funniest cartoon of the year didn't make the magazine as it co-incided with the weeks headline-
"Has Hill been dumped." I think dumped was an unfortunate turn of phrase, don't you?

JEAN ALESI — BENETTON'S LOOSE CANNON!
— MY MAN TO WIN AT HOCKENHEIM!

Well now after a year we know the answer about the Benetton Grand Prix car. It was all down to Schumacher

Well I still think it was a great idea Bernie, having three cars per team

Damon went through a phase during the year of going backwards at the starts and blamed it on his clutch!

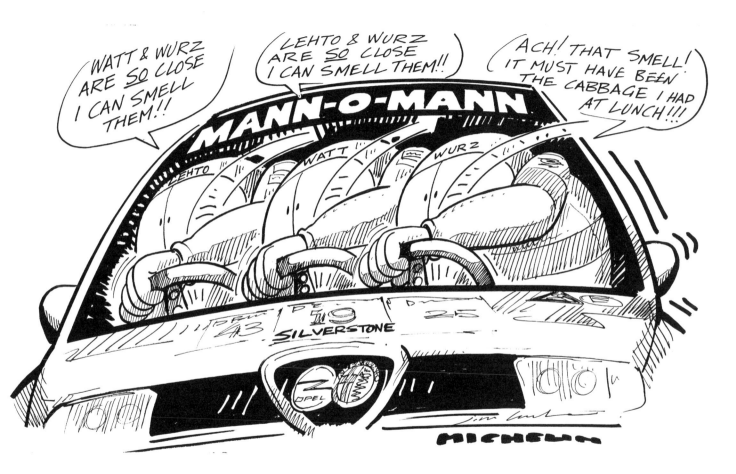

Sourkrauts

83

Michael Schumacher could win a Grand Prix on a dog!....Well, come to think of it......

At Spa the Williams boys really ****** up

Ave Caesar!

90

Nobody loves a smarty pants Andrew

I think we should draw a veil over this one

He'll overcharge you Damon, talk about his problems and then probably stuff it at the first corner

Bertie Fisher and Rory Kennedy, two of Ireland's best 'roadsweepers'

This was after Monza and those stupid bloody tyres. Formula One - the technological
peak of Motorsport? Do me a favour!

Okay so I was wrong, I wasn't the only one who thought Jordan had signed Damon.

Wow what a surprise. It was like Alan Shearer announcing he was going to play for Scunthorpe!

Hello ITV. You must be jolly excited at the prospect of all those <u>British</u> Grand Prix drivers
who will be contesting the F1 Championship in 1997

105

HILL
BE NICE-
FOSTER
NEW ED.
AUTOSPORT

Jordan........still looking

Oh! In Portugal it was **so close**!

HILL
DAVID C.
HAS
NOTHING
UP TOP

During the week leading up to the last Grand Prix of the season it seemed the whole country was willing Damon to win the Championship

HILL

BTCC-
AUDI
WINS
AGAIN

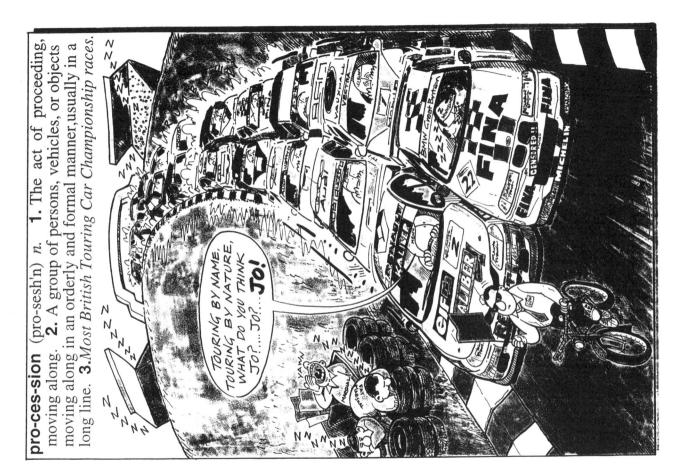

Come in number 43!

Yes I did stay up and watch it. But I was so tired I fell asleep and missed the start. I woke up just as Gerhard almost took Damon off on the 3rd lap. Wow that woke me up!

Can we predict that in 1997 this position will be reversed?

117

HILL
WALLACE
& GROMIT
LOST IN
NEW YORK

I have taken the mickey out of the Williams mechanics all year but their sportsmanship
and sense of fair play was without question. I am sure that in '97 they will treat Frentzen the same way
they treated Hill......*you happy with that Laurence? Can I run the cartoon now?*

I promise that in 1997 there will be 57 varieties of this joke

Martin Brundle spent all year perfecting his off-road rally skills,
in Melbourne......Brazil....... Imola......Hungary........

More uses for ex-Monza rubber

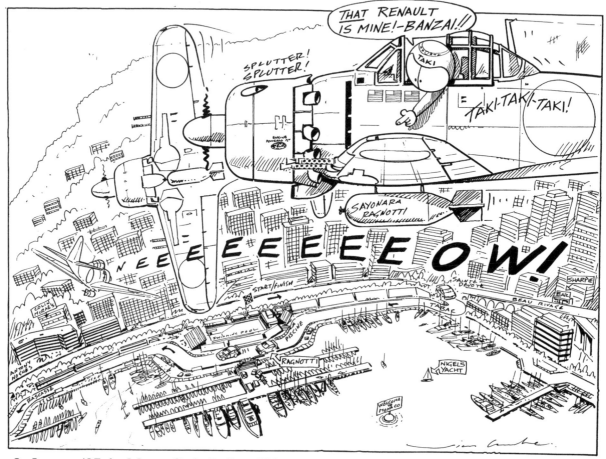

In January '97 the Monte Carlo Rally will have a superspecial on part of the Grand Prix circuit. The perfect opportunity for a certain Japanese gentleman to get his revenge on Jean Ragnotti